NICK FURY:
AGENT 110911

TOP-TIER S.H.I.E.L.D. OPERATIVE

SON OF NICK FURY SR.

FORMER SECRET AVENGER

LIKE HIS FATHER, FURY'S BLOOD CONTAINS THE POWERFUL INFINITY FORMULA SERUM THAT SLOWS HIS AGING, BUT IT IS THE YOUNGER FURY'S TRAINING AND SKILL THAT MAKE HIM INDISPENSABLE FOR HIGH-STAKES SOLO MISSIONS REQUIRING QUICK THINKING AND PRECISE ACTION.

NICK FURY

DEEP-COVER CAPERS

JAMES ROBINSON WRITER

ACO PENCILERS
WITH **HUGO PETRUS** (#4)

HUGO PETRUS INKER

RACHELLE ROSENBERG COLORIST

VC's **TRAVIS LANHAM** LETTERER

ACO COVER ART

MARK BASSO ASSOCIATE EDITOR

MARK PANICCIA EDITOR

NICK FURY CREATED BY **STAN LEE & JACK KIRBY**

COLLECTION EDITOR **JENNIFER GRÜNWALD**
ASSISTANT EDITOR **CAITLIN O'CONNELL**
ASSOCIATE MANAGING EDITOR **KATERI WOODY**
EDITOR, SPECIAL PROJECTS **MARK D. BEAZLEY**
VP PRODUCTION & SPECIAL PROJECTS **JEFF YOUNGQUIST**
SVP PRINT, SALES & MARKETING **DAVID GABRIEL**
BOOK DESIGNER **ADAM DEL RE**

EDITOR IN CHIEF **AXEL ALONSO**
CHIEF CREATIVE OFFICER **JOE QUESADA**
PRESIDENT **DAN BUCKLEY**
EXECUTIVE PRODUCER **ALAN FINE**

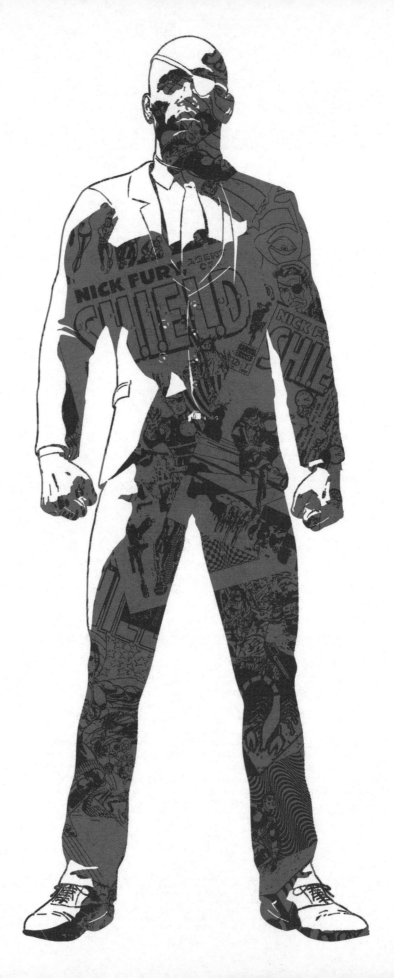

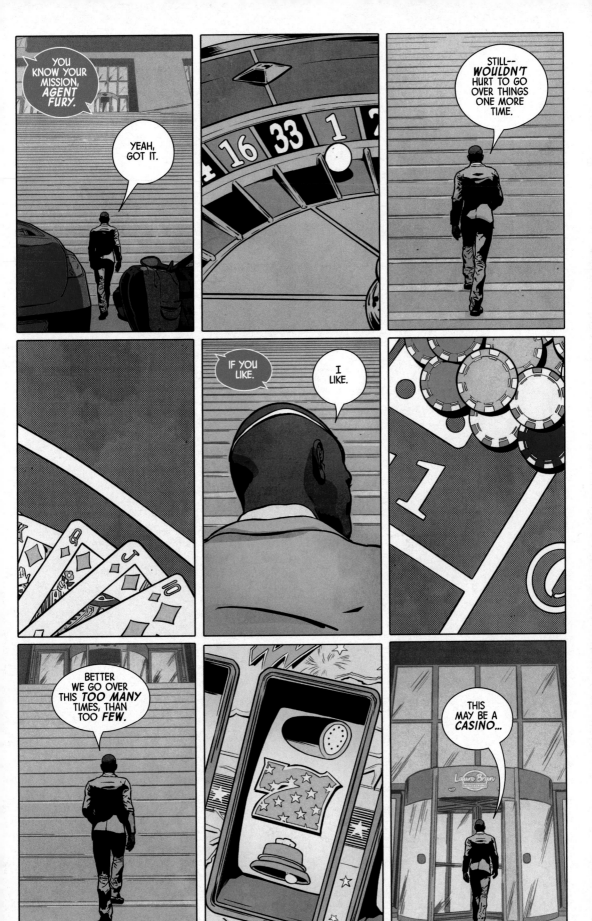

1

THE FRENCH RIVIERA.

Mission: To acquire data from the casino hotel penthouse of Auric Goodfellow, chief money-man for Hydra, regarding details of their illicit cash holdings.

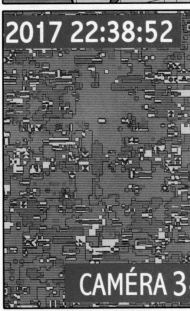

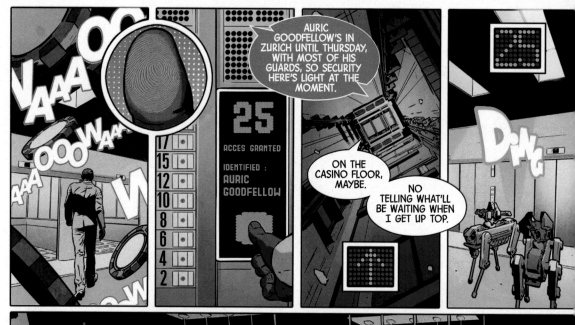

AURIC GOODFELLOW'S IN ZURICH UNTIL THURSDAY, WITH MOST OF HIS GUARDS, SO SECURITY HERE'S LIGHT AT THE MOMENT.

25

ACCES GRANTED

IDENTIFIED:
AURIC GOODFELLOW

ON THE CASINO FLOOR, MAYBE.

NO TELLING WHAT'LL BE WAITING WHEN I GET UP TOP.

NOW...

THERE. GOT A BEAD ON THE PRIZE.

THAT EYEPATCH COST ALMOST AS MUCH AS A HELICARRIER, SO I'D SURE HOPE IT'S GOOD FOR SOMETHING.

WHERE IS THE DATA?

HIDDEN SAFE. STATE-OF-THE-ART.

PATCH, SHOW COMBINATION.

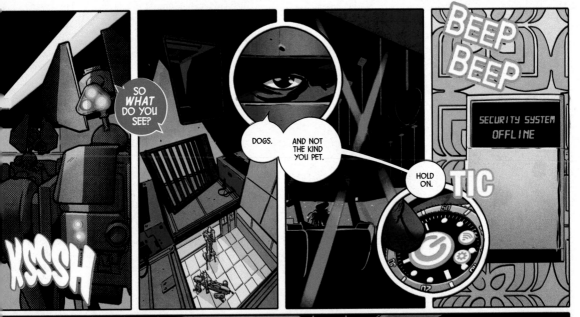

GREG LAND & **FRANK D'ARMATA**
NO. 1 VARIANT

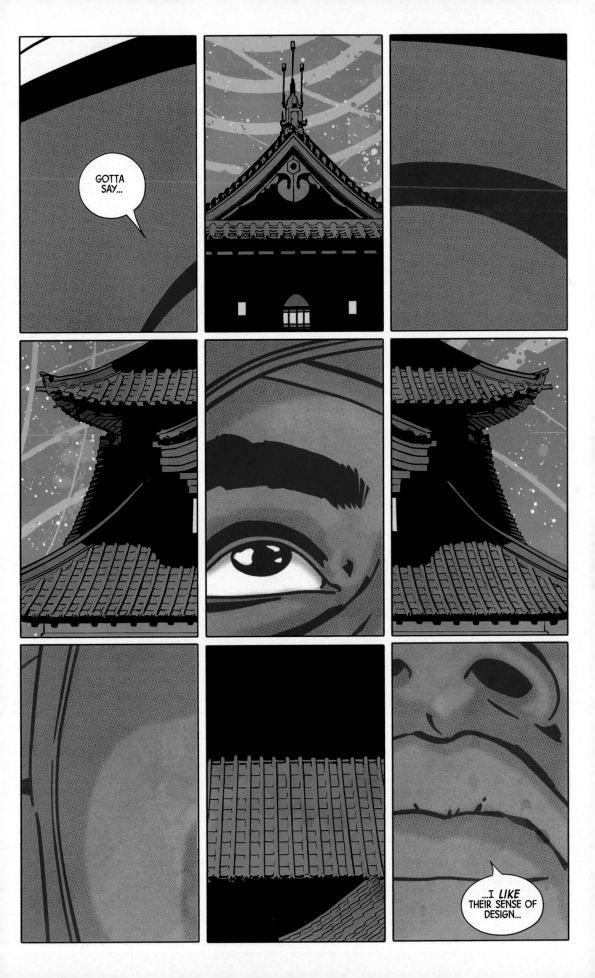

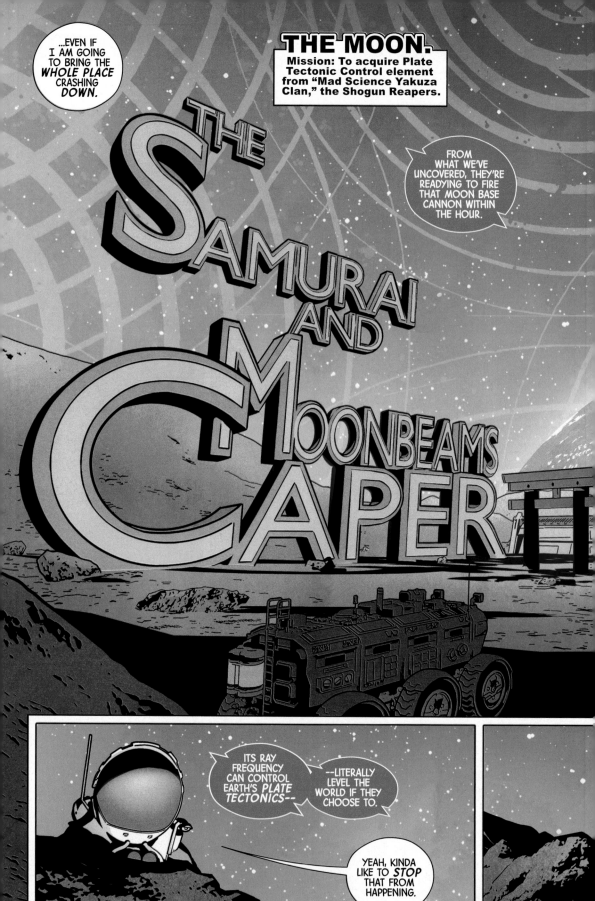

2

DISPERSE *PRISM DUST,* AGENT FURY.

ALREADY ON IT.

FSSSHHHHH

WARNING

警告

WARNING

<INTRUDER!>* DANNY KIKU-SAMA! <YOU SEE ON OUR CAMERAS!>

<I HAVE EYES.>

FURY JR. NICK.

<YOUR ORDERS, FEAR-SAMA. WHAT SHOULD WE DO?>

*TRANSLATED FROM JAPANESE.

DANIEL KIKU (A.K.A. DANNY FEAR).
High-ranking member of the Shogun Reapers Organization.

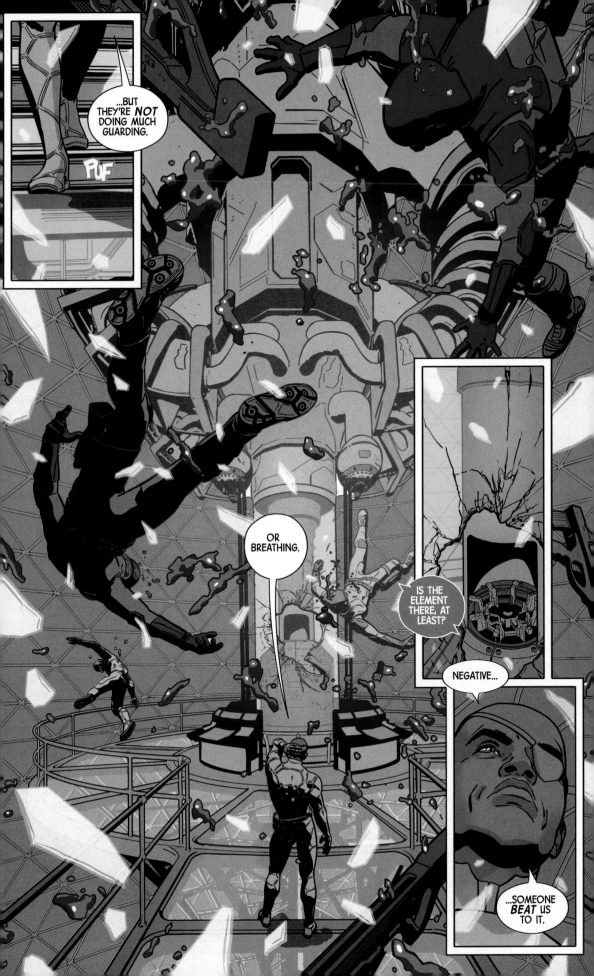

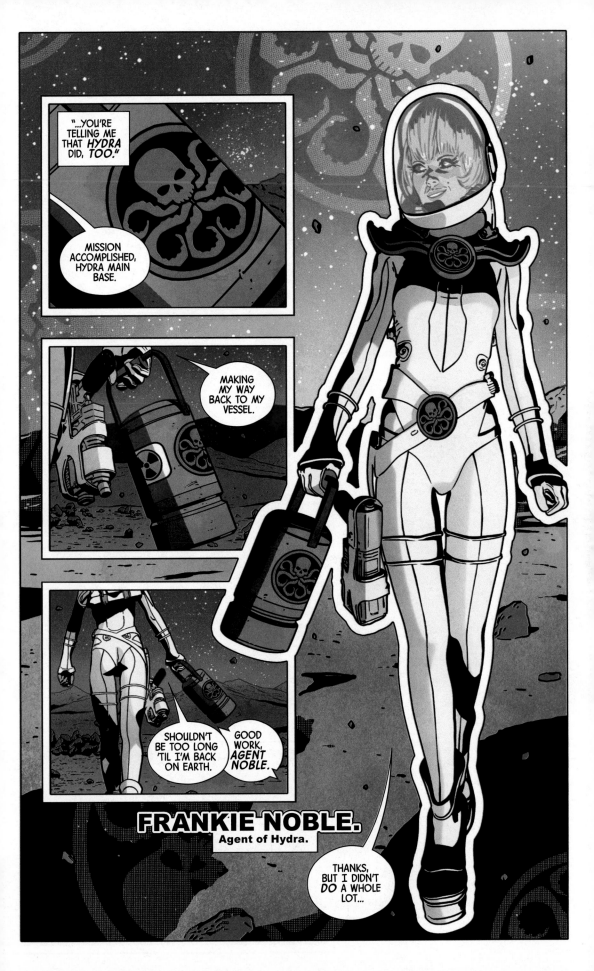

LARRY STROMAN, MARK MORALES & JASON KEITH
NO. 1 VARIANT

JOHN TYLER CHRISTOPHER
NO. 1 ACTION FIGURE VARIANT

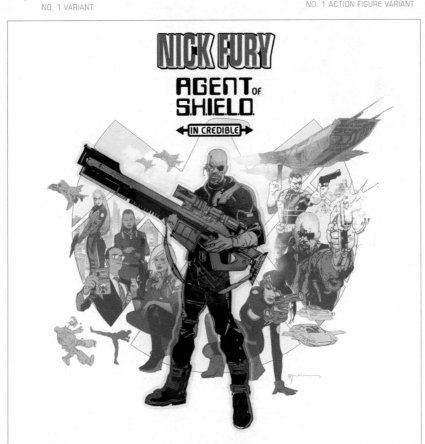

BILL SIENKIEWICZ
NO. 1 HIP-HOP VARIANT

NICK

THE ASSASSIN LOCO

Mission: On this inaugural trip of the Pan-South America Jaguar Limited--a high-speed rail line the length of the continent from the Mexican border to Tierra del Fuego--it is vital that the assassination of one of the dignitaries traveling on board is prevented.

MEXICO D

HOWEVER, THERE'S A *CARTEL* OR *THREE* THAT THE GENERAL WAS IN LEAGUE WITH WHO'D APPRECIATE THEIR OPERATIONS *NOT* GOING PUBLIC-- THEIR FEAR BEING SALVADORA WILL TRY TO STRIKE A DEAL.

BUT, WITH SO MANY SOUTH AMERICAN WORLD LEADERS MAKING THIS TRAIN TRIP, HE DECIDED TO NOT BE AMONG THEM WOULD BE TO LOSE FACE.

HE'S BEEN *UNTOUCHABLE* IN HIS OWN COUNTRY.

HE'S DETERMINED TO OUTDO THEM ALL-- OUT-DRINK, OUT-PARTY.

HE'S APPARENTLY OBLIVIOUS TO THE ARREST AWAITING HIM AT THE OTHER END-- OR TOO ARROGANT OR STUPID TO CARE.

SO, A CARTEL HITMAN?

YES, AT LEAST AS WE BELIEVE FOR THE MOMENT.

I'LL WORK WITH WHAT I HAVE.

HERE.

KSSSH

KNOCK KNOCK

'SCUSE.

PORTER, SIR.

CLUNK

CLUNK

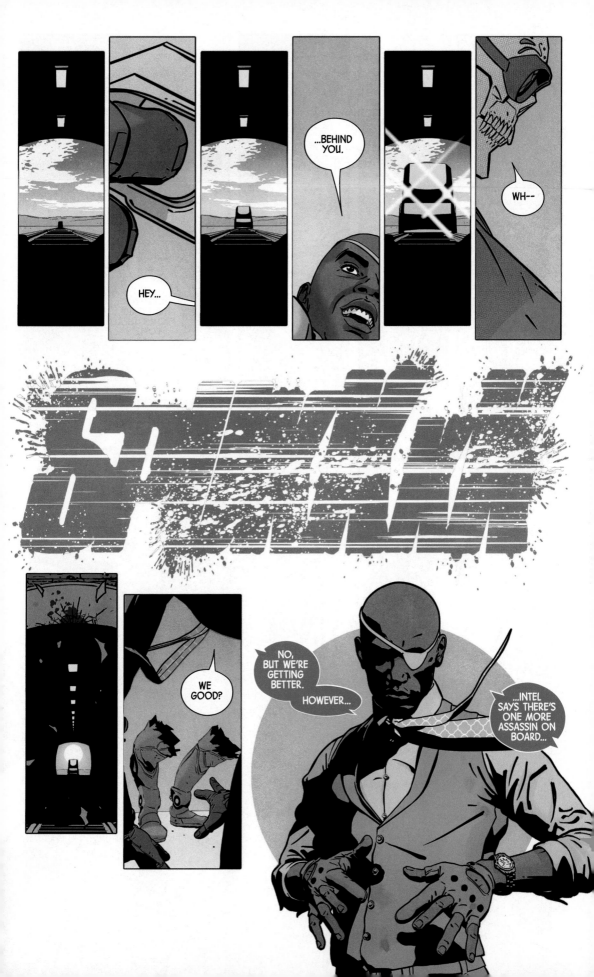

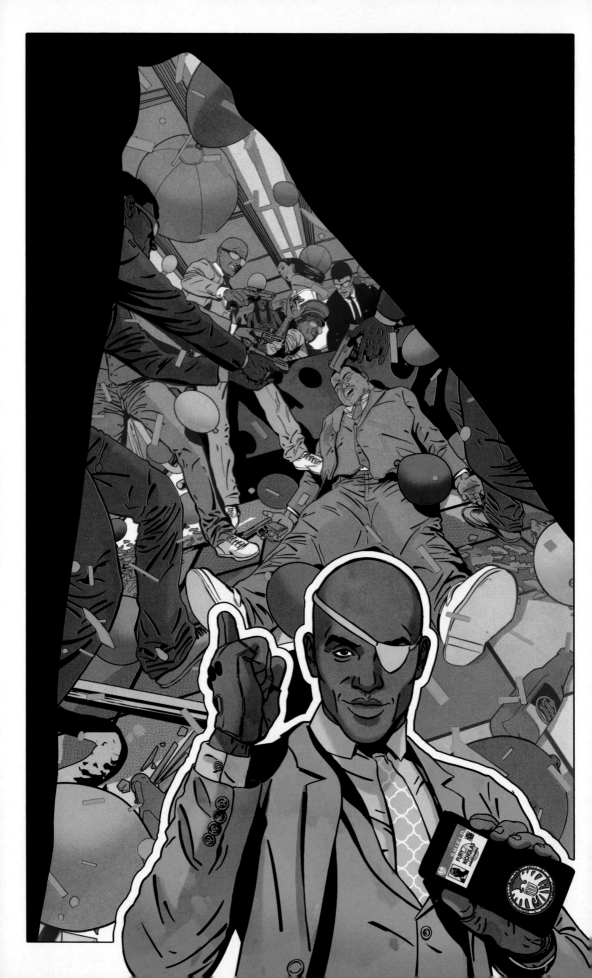

YOU JUST SHOT ONE OF SALVADORA'S OWN SECURITY.

YES, AN ASSASSIN PLANTED AS BACKUP FOR THE OTHERS.

NOW, MY QUESTION TO YOU...

...MELODIA *DIAS*--YES, I GOT INTEL ON YOU, TOO--

--IS WHY YOU HAVEN'T TOLD ME YOU WORK FOR THE *I.C.J.**

*INTERNATIONAL COURT OF JUSTICE.

I'M INCOGNITO, SILLY.

AND I COULD ASK THE SAME OF YOU, NICK FURY. *JUNIOR.* AGENT OF S.H.I.E.L.D.

MY JOB IS TO MAKE SURE THE GENERAL GETS TO ARGENTINA, WHERE MY PEOPLE ARE WAITING TO ARREST HIM.

BUT ALL YOU'VE DONE IS SIT THERE DRINKING HIGHBALLS. IF YOU HAVEN'T NOTICED, THERE'S BEEN AN ASSASSIN... OR SIX...ON BOARD.

YES, BUT I KNEW YOU WERE ON THE TRAIN TOO, DOING MY JOB FOR ME. THANK YOU, BY THE WAY.

YOU MADE ME TOO, *HUH?*

LIKE THAT'S HARD. YOU'RE A DISTINCTIVE GUY, ANYONE TOLD YOU THAT? SOMEONE MUST HAVE.

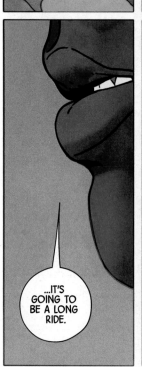

MARCO RUDY
NO. 2 VARIANT

4

READY FOR YOUR NEXT ASSIGNMENT, AGENT FURY?

YEAH, I'M READY. IN FACT, LET'S GO. WE'RE ON THE CLOCK.

YOU ARE, MORE ACCURATELY.

SIMPLY PUT, FAIL THIS MISSION...

FURY

ATLANTIS.
Mission: Infiltrate Atlantis and eliminate the Hydra spy who has been stealing crucial Atlantean intel since the city's reconstruction.

Mission addendum: To do this, you must use S.H.I.E.L.D.'s advanced "liquid breathing" technology, converting your lungs to "gills," allowing you to breathe underwater. However, keep in mind, Agent Fury, the time limit for your body's acceptance of its altered state--and therefore for this mission as a whole--is just 55 minutes.

54:52

THAT TOO, YES. THERE'S AN OPTIMISM THAT THE CITY CAN ENJOY A BRIGHT, NEW ERA.

TODAY MARKS A CELEBRATION.

KING BACK ON HIS THRONE.

THE PEOPLE WHO WERE SCATTERED HAVE ALL RETURNED. THE CITY'S SPIRES STAND TALL AGAIN.

SO ATLANTIS HAS A HYDRA SPY, LEAKING DATA COMPROMISING THE KINGDOM'S NATIONAL SECURITY.

THAT'S RIGHT. WE BELIEVE HYDRA'S END GOAL IS TO COERCE NAMOR AND HIS PEOPLE INTO ANOTHER GLOBAL CONFLICT.

49:03

HUH. AT LEAST ATTUMA'S OUT COLD.

HOW LONG WAS I OUT?

SEVENTEEN MINUTES NEAR AS.

I'M LOSING MY DISGUISE-- MY BLUE FACE--FLAKING RIGHT OFF ME. COMPLICATES THINGS.

I HAVE TO MOVE IT THEN IF I'M GOING TO FINISHED WHAT I STARTED...

...EVEN IF IT TAKES MY LAST BREATH.

WHERE ARE YOU NOW?

SIGNAL LOST

SOME KIND OF MAINTENANCE PASSAGEWAY BELOW THE BUILDING.

HAVE YOU LOCATED THE SPY?

NO, BUT IF I WERE A SPY, THIS IS WHERE I'D BE...

...DOING "REPAIRS" UNDERNEATH WHERE THE CITY'S DATA IS STORED.

02:43

"CELEBRATION OUTSIDE SAVED ME.

"EVERYONE WAS LOOKING AT NAMOR, I WAS ABLE TO GET AWAY.

"WOULD HAVE RAISED SOME EYEBROWS IF ANYONE HAS SEEN ME MAKING MY EXIT SUCKING ON THE AIR RESERVE IN MY SPEAR."

00:00

YOU WERE LUCKY.
YEAH, I WAS.
ONE THING ON MY MIND, THOUGH-- THE SPY WASN'T IN A FAKE POLYMER SKIN LIKE ME, HE WAS A REAL ATLANTEAN.
AND?
WHAT DO YOU MEAN "AND"? "HAIL HYDRA," HE SAID, FULL ON.
HYDRA IS RECRUITING ATLANTEANS?
OF COURSE. SO ARE WE.
YOU'RE TELLING ME S.H.I.E.L.D. HAS ATLANTEAN AGENTS, TOO?
WE'RE WORKING IN IT. IF THEY'D BEEN BETTER PLACED, WE WOULDN'T HAVE REQUIRED YOUR SERVICES.
AND NAMOR HAS NO IDEA?
LOOK, EVERYTHING I TOLD YOU WAS TRUE ABOUT THE HOPE THAT WE CAN MAKE ATLANTIS OUR ALLY...
...BUT NAMOR IS AND WILL ALWAYS... BE NAMOR.
SO IF I WERE YOU, I'D GET READY FOR ANY EVENTUALITY...
...BECAUSE S.H.I.E.L.D. CERTAINLY IS.
THE END

FERNANDO BLANCO
NO. 3 VARIANT

5

DINC

MORNING. HUNGRY, I BET.

WORLD NEWS

RAVENOUS.

EXIT

WHAT'LL IT BE?

COFFEE, BACON...AND I'M TOLD YOU HAVE THE BEST EGGS OVER EASY.

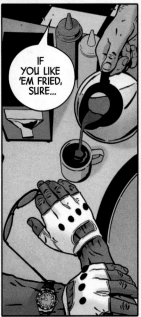

IF YOU LIKE 'EM FRIED, SURE...

...THEY'RE TO DIE FOR.

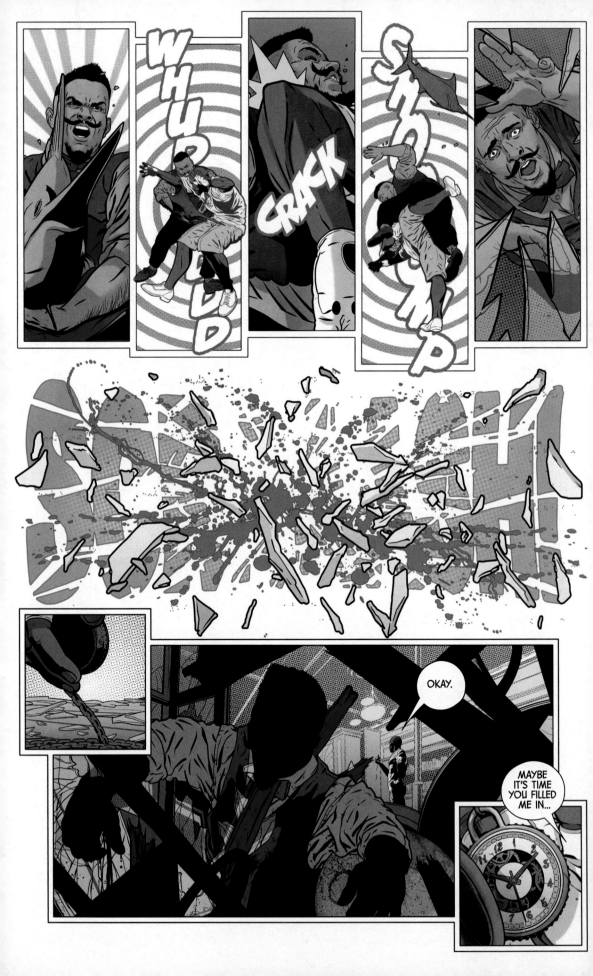

EDITOR'S NOTE: TO GET THE FULL EFFECT OF THIS PANORAMIC SCENE, PLACE 2 ISSUES SIDE BY SIDE FOR A 4-PAGE SPREAD LIKE ONLY ACO COULD BRING YOU!

KRUNK

LIKE I DID THE DAMN NEAR IMPOSSIBLE.

I GET IT. YOU WANT ME TO BE MY FATHER.

HONESTLY, WE'D BE HAPPY IF YOU WERE ONE-TENTH THE MAN HE WAS.

BUT BASICALLY... YES.

SO WHAT GRADE DID I GET TODAY?

INCOMPLETE.

WHAT?

GAS

YOU FORGOT SOMEONE...

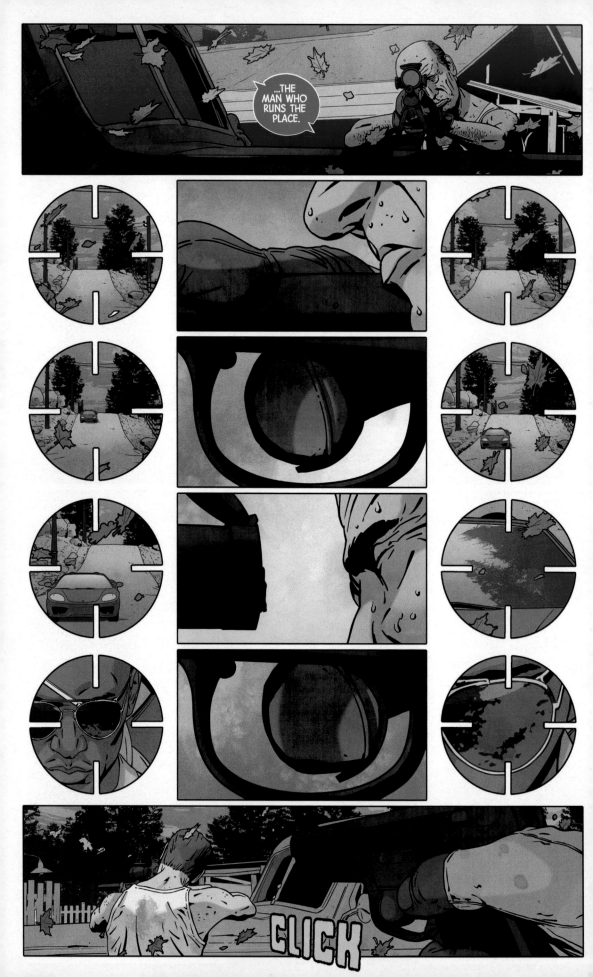

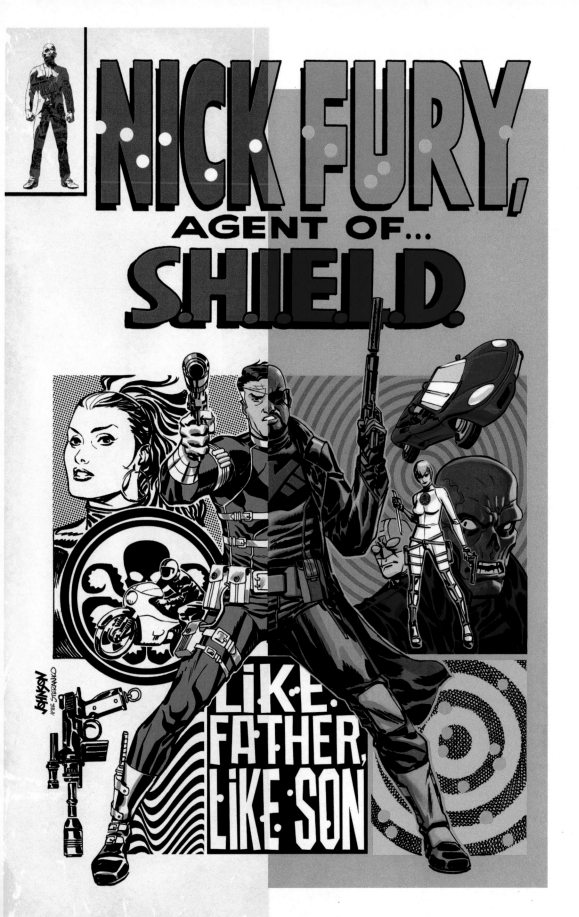

DAVE JOHNSON
NO. 6 HOMAGE VARIANT

FURY?

AGENT FURY, CAN YOU HEAR ME?

OF COURSE I CAN, YOU'VE BEEN YELLING IN MY EAR FOR THE PAST HOUR.

WELL, YOU HAVEN'T RESPONDED IN THE LAST HOUR AND A HALF, SO WHO'S THE BAD GUY, HUH?

THAT'S WHAT I'M HERE TO FIND OUT. HUH.

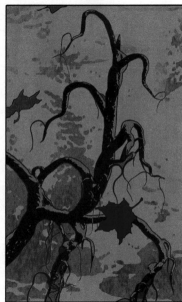

SORRY, I'VE BEEN QUIET, IT'S JUST WEIRD LOOKING AROUND--

--THE MAULED BODY ON THE CASTLE GROUNDS--

--SEEING THE SAME THINGS MY DAD SAW, I IMAGINE.

AND TRYING TO SOLVE A MYSTERY...

NICK

"...THAT WE ALL THOUGHT MY *FATHER* HAD ALREADY *SOLVED.*"

THE RETURN TO RAVENLOO

MISSION:
Solve the murder.
Find the truth.

THANK YOU FOR BEING SO ACCOMMODATING, MS. MacGREGOR.

PLEASE, CALL ME *RACHEL.* AND OF COURSE I'LL HELP YOU. I WELCOME YOUR HELP TOO, FOR THAT MATTER. A MAN HAS BEEN KILLED AND ANSWERS MUST BE GOTTEN.

YES, FOR "WHO, WHY AND HOW."

I ALREADY DID SOME RESEARCH ON THE FLIGHT IN-- THIS ISN'T THE FIRST RECENT KILLING BY THE "HOUND," RIGHT?

NO, THERE WAS *ANOTHER* VICTIM BEFORE THIS--A *WOMAN.* MUCH MORE GRISLY THAN THIS ONE, SO I WAS TOLD.

THAT'S WHY I CAME SO QUICKL I KNEW THAT FIRST VICTIM, SON OF--THIS DEAD MAN, TOO.

THE GIRL'S NAME IS--WAS-- *FRANKIE NOBLE.* A HYDRA AGENT I ENCOUNTERED IN THE PAST.

AS FOR THIS GUY, *AURIC GOODFELLOW*--HE WAS HYDRA, TOO ONE OF THE *MONEY MEN* WHO HANDLED THEIR FINANCES.

BOTH OF THEM HYDRA? SO THEY WERE ASSOCIATES?

OF
EACH OTHER?
OH, THEY WERE
AS THICK AS
THIEVES.

IT'S
GETTING COLD,
LET'S GO
INSIDE.

BEING
BLIND, I
WOULDN'T
KNOW.

I INHERITED
THE CASTLE FROM ALISTAIR
RAMPSON, THE LAST OWNER--WHO
GOT IT AFTER YOUR FATHER KILLED LORD
GAVIN RAVENLOCK, THE MAN PARTLY
BEHIND THE WHOLE "HELLHOUND"
CHARADE THAT FIRST TIME.

I'M
ALONE, WITH
NOTHING
BUT GHOSTS
TO KEEP ME
COMPANY
NOW.

GHOSTS?

HA--A
METAPHOR. I HAD
PSYCHIC ABILITIES
AT ONE TIME--
AT LEAST THATS
WHAT PEOPLE
TOLD ME.

NO MORE,
THOUGH.

WHAT ARE YOU DOING?

WELL I'M CERTAINLY NOT GOING INTO TOWN.

THE CASTLE AND ITS GROUNDS HIDE MORE SECRETS, I KNOW THAT.

SHIK

TIC

WHUP

THE HELLHOUND WAS A *FAKE* THAT TIME BEFORE WITH MY DAD, SO WHY SHOULD IT BE ANY DIFFERENT NOW?

SO WHY PRETEND TO LEAVE? TO PROTECT MS. MacGREGOR IF YOU RAN INTO TROUBLE?

PROTECT HER? *ERR...*NOT EXACTLY.

SHUN

TIC

...FRANKIE NOBLE, AGENT OF HYDRA!

YOU SAW THROUGH MY DISGUISE?

ALMOST IMMEDIATELY. I MAY ONLY HAVE ONE EYE, BUT I'M NOT BLIND LIKE RACHEL. NOT DEAF, EITHER--YOUR SCOTTISH ACCENT'S TERRIBLE.

BUT I WANTED TO SEE WHAT THIS WAS ALL ABOUT FIRST.

WHERE IS RACHEL, BY THE WAY--THE REAL RACHEL?

DEAD, OF COURSE. SHE HAD TO PLAY *ME* AS THE HOUND'S FIRST VICTIM. THAT'S WHY HER MAULING WAS MORE SEVERE, TO HIDE WHO SHE REALLY WAS.

AND AS TO WHY I DIDN'T ATTACK YOU OR KILL YOU EARLIER WHEN I HAD THE CHANCE?

WHERE WOULD BE THE FUN OF THAT?

REMEMBER THAT SEISMIC DEVICE THAT SLIPPED THROUGH YOUR FINGERS ON THE MOON?

THAT WAS YOU?

GREAT BRITAIN'S ABOUT TO BECOME ONE GREAT BIG HYDRA BASE...OR WE'LL LEVEL THE WHOLE ISLAND.

YOU'RE CRAZY.

NO, I'M-- UM--YEAH, PERHAPS I AM. AIN'T IT GRAND?

BUT WHY KILL "YOURSELF" AND AURIC GOODFELLOW?

AFTER YOU TOOK HIS FILES ON HYDRA'S FINANCES, HE STOPPED BEING AN ASSET. MORE A LIABILITY.

AND I KNEW IF HE DIED HERE, YOU'D COME SNIFFING ABOUT.

AFTER WHAT HAPPENED HERE WITH YOUR FATHER, HOW COULD YOU HELP YOURSELF? ESPECIALLY IF I BROUGHT THE HOUND BACK INTO PLAY.

I'M *FLATTERED* YOU RECOGNIZED ME.

"KNOW YOUR ENEMIES." BESIDES, YOU'RE A HYDRA AGENT BIG ON WIGS AND DRAMA, SO YOU WEREN'T HARD TO IDENTIFY. IT WAS EITHER YOU...OR STRUCKER GOING ON A BLIND DATE.

SO, I GET THE "WHO" OF THIS NOW, OBVIOUSLY. *YOU.* HYDRA.

"HOW." CREATE AN ARTIFICIAL HOUND, KILL POOR RACHEL AND MOVE IN UNDER HER PLACE.

"WHY," I STILL DON'T SEE, THOUGH.

O THIS WAS PARTLY A *LURE* TO \|AIL ME? *I'M* FLATTERED, TOO. KIND OF RISKY, THOUGH, YOU ASK ME--

I WASN'T ASKING YOU, THOUGH, NICKY-BOY.

FROM WHERE I STAND, MY GAMBLE PAID OFF.

HERE YOU ARE CAPTURED, UNPREPARED AND OUTGUNNED.

HUH. YEAH. LOOKS THAT WAY.

TIC

EXCEPT, AS YOU MENTIONED, I'M THE SON OF MY FATHER.

I'M NICK FURY, JR. AND LIKE MY DAD...